Party
Pants

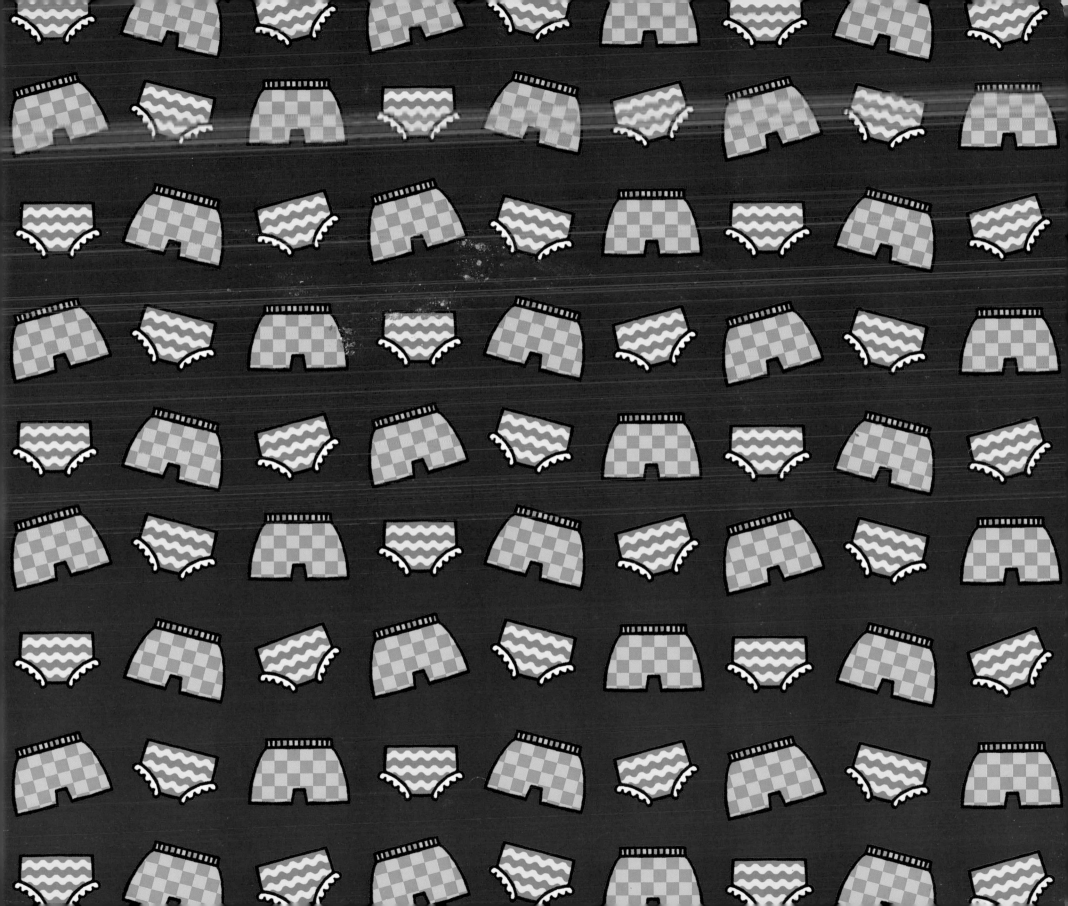

PUFFIN BOOKS

UK | USA | Canada | Ireland | Australia
India | New Zealand | South Africa

Puffin Books is part of the Penguin Random House group of companies
whose addresses can be found at global.penguinrandomhouse.com.

www.penguin.co.uk   www.puffin.co.uk   www.ladybird.co.uk

Penguin
Random House
UK

First published as *More Pants* by David Fickling Books 2007
Published by Picture Corgi 2008
Published in this edition as *Party Pants* by Puffin Books 2019
001

Printed in China
A CIP catalogue record for this book is available from the British Library

ISBN: 978-0-241-38463-3
All correspondence to:
Puffin Books, Penguin Random House Children's
80 Strand, London WC2R ORL

Party Pants

Giles Andreae
Nick Sharratt

PUFFIN

For Jackson – G.A.

For Pam, Maya and Sienna – N.S.

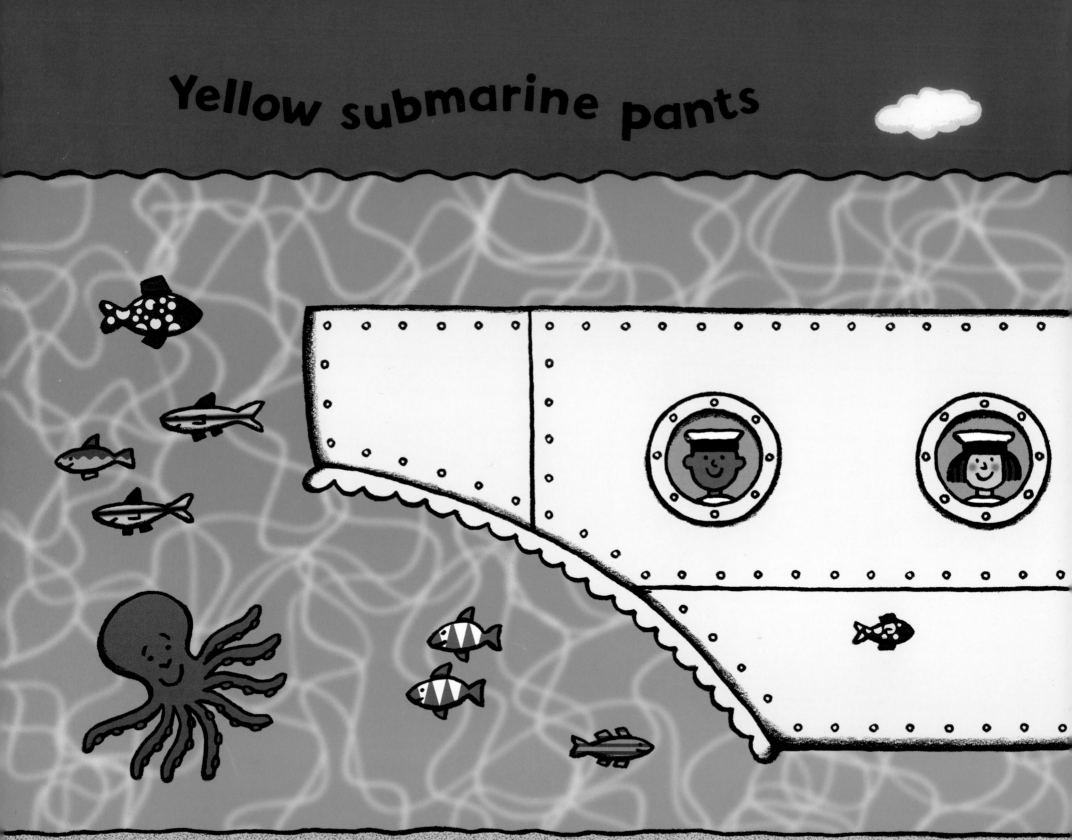

Yellow submarine pants

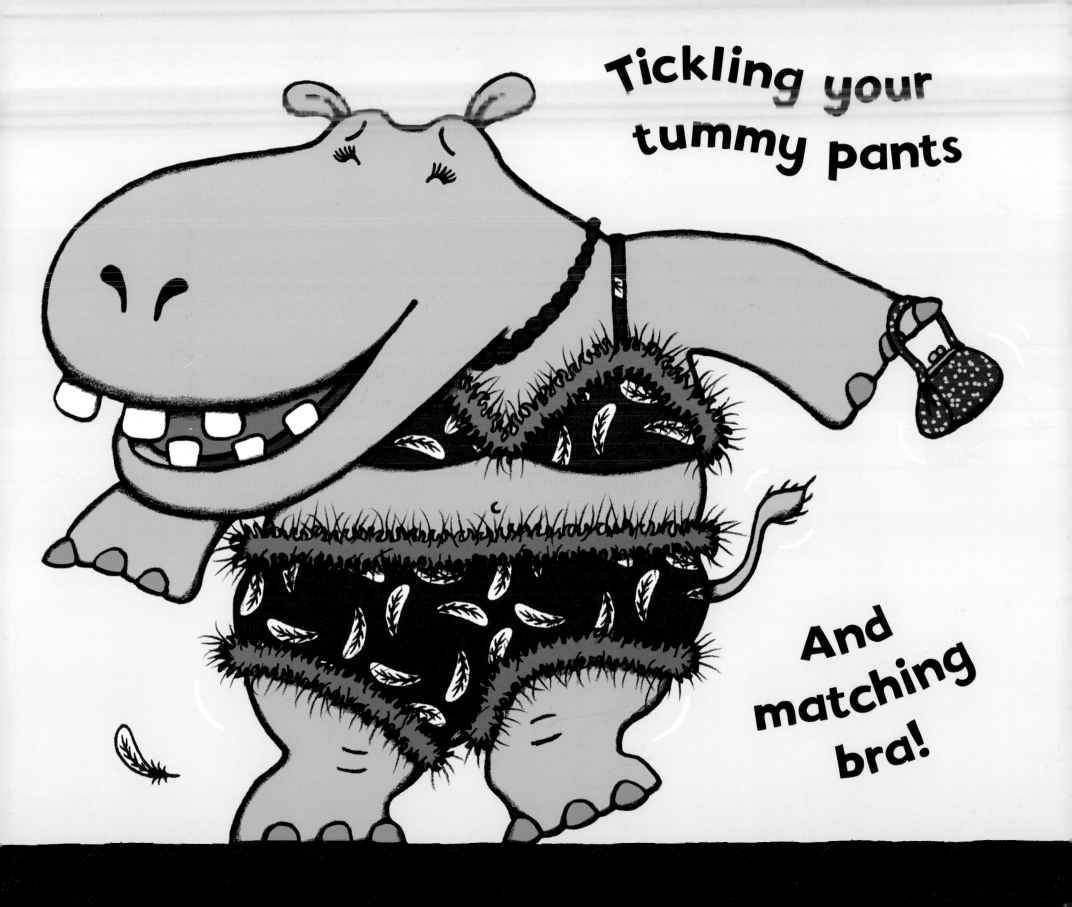

Tickling your tummy pants

And matching bra!

Arty pants,
party pants

Black belt in
karate pants

Stretchy pants
for fitting an
extra-special
mate in

Puffy pants, fluffy pants

Pants
for a
scary
dinosaur

Colder pants,

hotter pants

Aren't there
such a lotta pants?

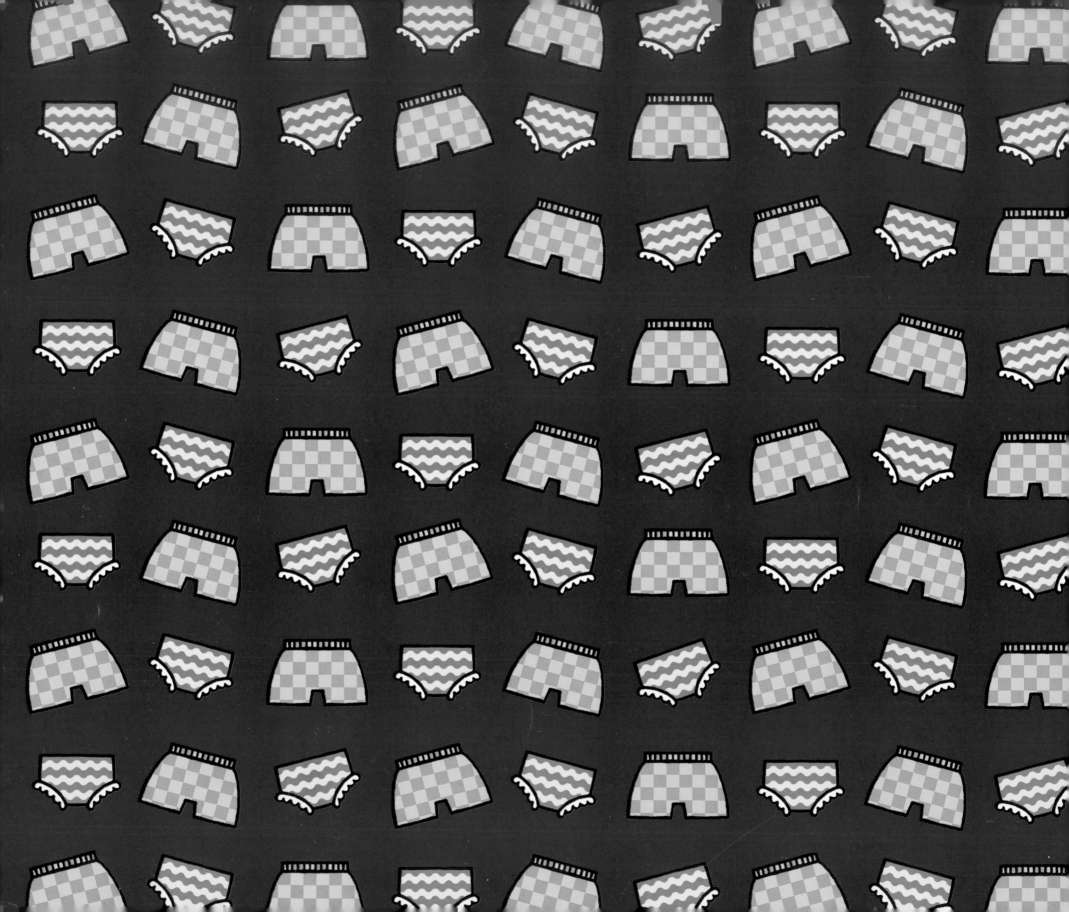

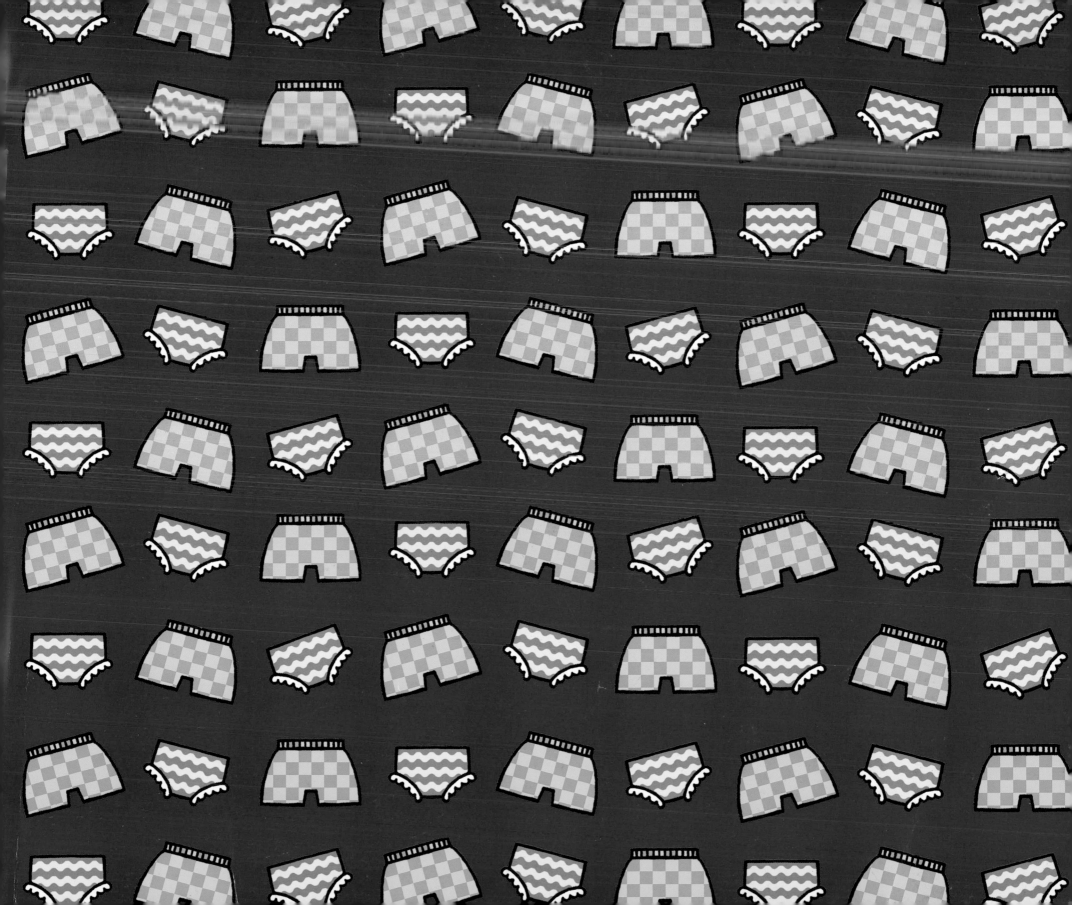

More books written by Giles Andreae

NOODLE HEAD!
The NAUGHTY book about being NICE
Giles Andreae
Illustrated by Lalalimola

Captain Flinn and the Pirate Dinosaurs
Giles Andreae and Russell Ayto

Captain Flinn and the Pirate Dinosaurs
The Magic Cutlass
Giles Andreae and Russell Ayto

Captain Flinn and the Pirate Dinosaurs
Missing Treasure!
Giles Andreae and Russell Ayto

Captain Flinn and the Pirate Dinosaurs
Smugglers Bay
Giles Andreae and Russell Ayto

Sir Scallywag and the GOLDEN UNDERPANTS
Giles Andreae & Korky Paul

Sir Scallywag and the DEADLY DRAGON POO
Giles Andreae & Korky Paul

Sir Scallywag and the BATTLE of STINKY BOTTOM
Giles Andreae and Korky Paul

and illustrated by Nick Sharratt

YOU CHOOSE
Nick Sharratt   Pippa Goodhart
A NEW STORY EVERY TIME – what will YOU CHOOSE?

YOU CHOOSE IN SPACE
Nick Sharratt   Pippa Goodhart
A NEW STORY EVERY TIME – what will YOU CHOOSE?

YOU CHOOSE YOUR DREAMS
Nick Sharratt   Pippa Goodhart
A NEW STORY EVERY TIME – what will YOU CHOOSE?

Shark in the Park!
Nick Sharratt

Shark in the Dark!
Nick Sharratt

Shark in the Park on a Windy Day!
Nick Sharratt